By
Tony Tallarico

kidsbooks®

WHERE ARE THEY?

FIND FREDDIE: AROUND THE WORLD

TIME TRAVELER

LOOK FOR LISA: TIME TRAVELER

SEARCH FOR SYLVESTER

WHERE'S WENDY?

I'M CHARLES OF THE CHIMPS!

THIS IS YOUR PA... ...KEEP IT CLEAN!

YOU ARE

FOR RENT

DIG WE MUS

DO... DARE... ME.

A GUTTER BALL!

TELEPHON

Travel the world to find Freddie.

Travel through time to look for Lisa.

Search high and low for Sylvester.

Find out where Wendy could possibly be!

FREDDIE

LISA

WENDY

SYLVESTER

FIND FREDDIE AROUND THE WORLD

Freddie has won an around the world vacation…and you're invited to come along! Stay close to Freddie, or you might get lost!

FIND FREDDIE IN THE UNITED STATES AND…

- ☐ Balloons (2)
- ☐ Barn
- ☐ Brooms (2)
- ☐ Buffalo
- ☐ Cactus (4)
- ☐ Campfire
- ☐ Cannon
- ☐ Cows (2)
- ☐ Coyote
- ☐ Footballs (2)
- ☐ Ghost
- ☐ Goat
- ☐ Guitars (2)
- ☐ Hockey player
- ☐ Jack-o´-lantern
- ☐ Kite
- ☐ Lighthouse
- ☐ Log cabin
- ☐ Moose
- ☐ Owl
- ☐ Periscope
- ☐ Scarecrows (2)
- ☐ Star
- ☐ Statue of Liberty
- ☐ Surfer
- ☐ Turtle
- ☐ Witch

Where did the elephant escape from?
Who is sleeping?
Where is Cuba?
What's on sale?
Where's the big cheese?

Freddie is northward bound as he travels to Canada, Alaska, Greenland, and Iceland.

FIND FREDDIE IN THIS WINTER WONDERLAND AND...

- ☐ Automobile
- ☐ Banana peel
- ☐ Bear
- ☐ Beaver
- ☐ Birds (2)
- ☐ Bone
- ☐ Box
- ☐ Bucket
- ☐ Elephant
- ☐ Elf
- ☐ Horse
- ☐ Ice-cream cone
- ☐ Igloo
- ☐ Jackrabbit
- ☐ Jester
- ☐ King Kong
- ☐ Lumberjack
- ☐ Mounty
- ☐ Oil well
- ☐ Pencil
- ☐ Pumpkin
- ☐ Scarecrow
- ☐ Seal
- ☐ Sleds (2)
- ☐ Snow castle
- ☐ Snowmen (2)
- ☐ Stars (2)
- ☐ Top hat
- ☐ Totem pole
- ☐ Unicycles

Where did Freddie take French lessons?
What's the 49th state?
Where's Greenland?
What's the capital of Canada?
Where's Nova Scotia?

Freddie heads southeast to the next three stops on his world tour: Ireland, Scotland, and England.

FIND FREDDIE IN THE BRITISH ISLES AND...

- ☐ Airplane
- ☐ Bagpiper
- ☐ Boats (7)
- ☐ Book
- ☐ Broom
- ☐ Bus
- ☐ Chicken
- ☐ Crown
- ☐ Dog
- ☐ Fish (8)
- ☐ Four-leaf clovers (4)
- ☐ Guitar
- ☐ Harp
- ☐ Horseshoe
- ☐ Kite
- ☐ Knight
- ☐ Magnifying glass
- ☐ Periscope
- ☐ Pig
- ☐ Pot of gold
- ☐ Sheep (3)
- ☐ Spear
- ☐ Stonehenge
- ☐ Telescope
- ☐ Turtle
- ☐ Umbrella

What games are they playing? (4)
What's for sale? (2)
Where's France?
Who did Freddie visit in Ireland?

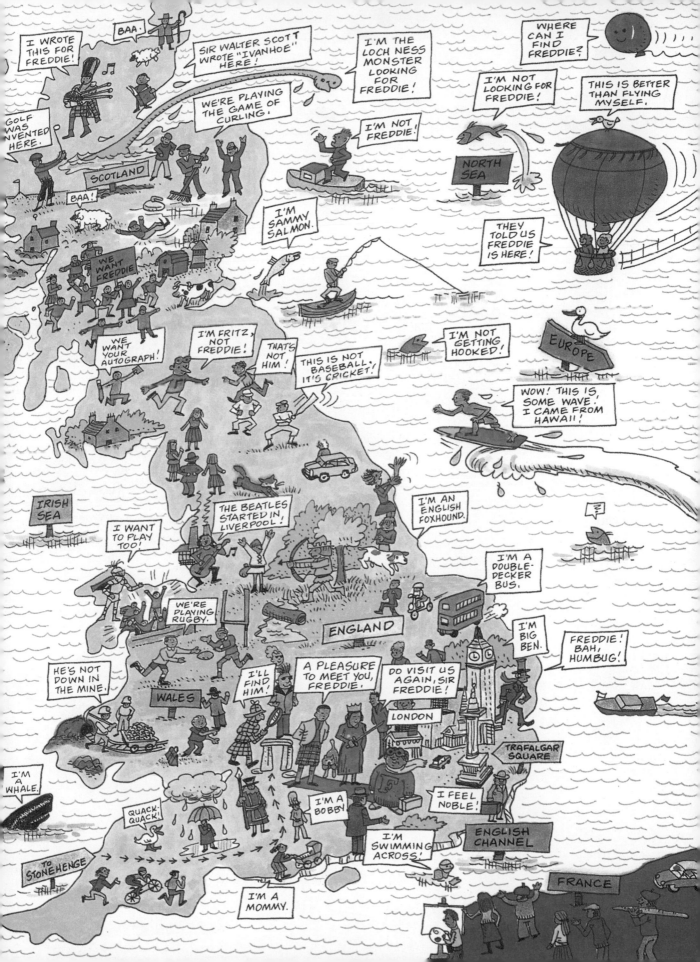

Freddie travels on throughout Europe...and you go along with him!

FIND FREDDIE AMONG THESE FRIENDLY FOREIGNERS AND...

☐ Artist
☐ Bather
☐ Beachball
☐ Bone
☐ Bull
☐ Camel
☐ Castle
☐ Dogs (2)
☐ Envelope
☐ Fire hydrant
☐ Heart
☐ Jack-o´-lantern
☐ Key
☐ Laundry
☐ Lost and Found
☐ Motorcycle
☐ Mountain goat
☐ Pencil
☐ Rabbit
☐ Sailboats (2)
☐ Santa Claus
☐ Skier
☐ Snowmen (2)
☐ Stars (2)
☐ Stork
☐ Tulip
☐ Turtles (2)
☐ Volcano
☐ Witch

Who was forgotten?
What gets wet?
Where do pandas live?
Where's the Strait of Gibraltar?

Next, Freddie is off to explore the largest continent, Asia. There are many things here that he's always wanted to see.

FIND FREDDIE IN THIS VAST AND EXOTIC LAND AND...

- ☐ Accordian player
- ☐ Balloon
- ☐ Bears (2)
- ☐ Birdcage
- ☐ Candy cane
- ☐ Chef
- ☐ Dragons (2)
- ☐ Fan
- ☐ Flying carpet
- ☐ Genie
- ☐ Heart
- ☐ Horse
- ☐ Kite
- ☐ Lemming
- ☐ Nutmeg tree
- ☐ Pandas (3)
- ☐ Peacock
- ☐ Reindeer
- ☐ Rice field
- ☐ Snakes (2)
- ☐ Surfer
- ☐ Tea cup
- ☐ Tears
- ☐ Telescope
- ☐ Tigers (2)
- ☐ Tire
- ☐ Turtle
- ☐ Water buffalo
- ☐ Yak

Where is the highest place on earth?
Which way is the North Pole?
Where's Japan?
Who needs the oasis?

Freddie's next stop is a continent filled with amazing animals. I hope he doesn't get into any trouble there.

FIND FREDDIE IN THIS AFRICAN ADVENTURE-LAND AND...

☐ Aardvark
☐ Automobile
☐ Book
☐ Boot
☐ Bottle
☐ Camels (2)
☐ Cape buffalo
☐ Cape seal
☐ Crocodile
☐ Cup
☐ Date palm
☐ Drum
☐ Giraffes (2)
☐ Gnu
☐ Gorilla
☐ Heart
☐ Huts (4)
☐ Ibis
☐ Leopard
☐ Light bulb
☐ Monkeys (3)
☐ Ostrich
☐ Pelican
☐ Penguin
☐ Porcupine
☐ Rhino
☐ Snakes (3)
☐ Sunglasses (4)
☐ Top hat
☐ TV antennas (2)
☐ Umbrella

Who's the king of the jungle?
Who's wearing stripes?
Where's the Suez Canal?

Freddie arrives in Australia and takes a very interesting ride. He'll stop off in New Zealand, New Guinea, and Tasmania, too.

FIND FREDDIE IN THE LAND DOWN UNDER AND...

- ☐ Barbell
- ☐ Baseball bat
- ☐ Book
- ☐ Boomerang
- ☐ Chef
- ☐ Crane
- ☐ Dingo
- ☐ Dragon
- ☐ Fishermen (2)
- ☐ Football
- ☐ Ghost
- ☐ Golfer
- ☐ Horse
- ☐ Jogger
- ☐ Kite
- ☐ Koalas (3)
- ☐ Lost shorts
- ☐ Lost sock
- ☐ Lyrebird
- ☐ Paper airplane
- ☐ Rabbits (4)
- ☐ Scuba diver
- ☐ Shark fins (5)
- ☐ Sheep (4)
- ☐ Skateboard
- ☐ Stars (3)
- ☐ Tennis players (4)
- ☐ Tent
- ☐ Tire
- ☐ Tree kangaroo
- ☐ Umbrella
- ☐ Wombat

Which three birds can't fly?
What's on sale?
Where's the Great Barrier Reef?

Freddie's next stop is the continent that surrounds the South Pole—Antarctica! It's the coldest place in the world. Is Freddie dressed for it?

FIND FREDDIE IN THIS BLISTERY BLIZZARD AND...

- ☐ Artist
- ☐ Balloon
- ☐ Beachball
- ☐ Bottle
- ☐ Camel
- ☐ Chair
- ☐ Chef
- ☐ Earmuffs
- ☐ Fish (2)
- ☐ Icebergs (4)
- ☐ Jester
- ☐ Key
- ☐ Lost boot
- ☐ Lost mitten
- ☐ Magnifying glass
- ☐ Mailbox
- ☐ Palm tree
- ☐ Penguins (10)
- ☐ Pick
- ☐ Refrigerator
- ☐ Seals (4)
- ☐ Shovel
- ☐ Skaters (3)
- ☐ Snowmen (2)
- ☐ South Pole
- ☐ Surfboard
- ☐ Telescope
- ☐ Tents (4)
- ☐ Tire
- ☐ Whales (4)

What two things are for sale?
Who's from another planet?

Watch out fourth largest continent, Freddie is coming to visit!

FIND FREDDIE IN SOUTH AMERICA AND...

- [ ] Alpaca
- [ ] Anteater
- [ ] Bear
- [ ] Binoculars
- [ ] Bone
- [ ] Bus
- [ ] Cactus
- [ ] Coffee pot
- [ ] Cowboy
- [ ] Flamingos (2)
- [ ] Flying bats (2)
- [ ] Guitar
- [ ] Hammock
- [ ] Jeep
- [ ] Monkeys (3)
- [ ] Motorcyle
- [ ] Orchid
- [ ] Periscope
- [ ] Pineapple
- [ ] Rain slicker
- [ ] Santa Claus
- [ ] Snakes (4)
- [ ] Swamp deer
- [ ] Tires (2)
- [ ] Toucans (2)
- [ ] Tree frog
- [ ] Turtles (2)
- [ ] TV antenna
- [ ] Umbrellas (2)
- [ ] Wagon

What is the longest mountain range in the world?
What's a three-sided nut?

Freddie extends his stay in South America and then heads north to Central America.

FIND FREDDIE IN BETWEEN NORTH AND SOUTH AMERICA AND...

- ☐ Aliens (2)
- ☐ Balloons (2)
- ☐ Banana boat
- ☐ Bathtub
- ☐ Bullfighter
- ☐ Butterfly
- ☐ Candle
- ☐ Flamingo
- ☐ Frog
- ☐ Iron
- ☐ Jogger
- ☐ Oil well
- ☐ Paper airplane
- ☐ Periscope
- ☐ Pirate
- ☐ Pot
- ☐ Roller skates
- ☐ Rowboat
- ☐ Sailboats (4)
- ☐ Shark fin
- ☐ Sled
- ☐ Snowman
- ☐ Straw
- ☐ Super hero
- ☐ Surfer
- ☐ Sword
- ☐ Traffic cop
- ☐ Truck
- ☐ Water-skier

Which is the largest country in Central America?
What two countries share the same island?
What's for sale? (2)
What country is separated by a canal?

It looks like some aliens have been following Freddie on his trip. Maybe they're planning to take him home with them.

FIND FREDDIE ON HIS LAST STOP AND...

- ☐ Alarm clock
- ☐ Basketball net
- ☐ Bathtub
- ☐ Bowling ball
- ☐ Castle
- ☐ Chair
- ☐ Firecracker
- ☐ Fish (8)
- ☐ Flamingo
- ☐ Giraffe
- ☐ Hot dog
- ☐ Igloo
- ☐ Jack-in-the-box
- ☐ Jack-o´-lantern
- ☐ Jackrabbit
- ☐ Kite
- ☐ Knight
- ☐ Lost ice skate
- ☐ Moose
- ☐ Owl
- ☐ Pencil
- ☐ Shark fins (2)
- ☐ Shipwrecked sailor
- ☐ Skier
- ☐ Sleds (2)
- ☐ Snowman
- ☐ Surfer
- ☐ Tepee
- ☐ Turtle
- ☐ TV antennas (3)
- ☐ Umbrella
- ☐ Walrus

Where has the walrus never been?
What country is Siberia next to?

Freddie has finally come home. All his "Where Are They?" friends are happy to see him!

FIND FREDDIE AND...

- ☐ Baseball cap
- ☐ Book
- ☐ Candy cane
- ☐ Cheese
- ☐ Dish
- ☐ Feather
- ☐ Fork
- ☐ Four-leaf clover
- ☐ Hearts (2)
- ☐ Letter
- ☐ Lost sock
- ☐ Pig
- ☐ Rug
- ☐ Slipper
- ☐ Star

What's for sale?
Who missed
  Freddie the most?

**FIND FREDDIE
AROUND THE WORL**

LOOK FOR LISA: TIME TRAVELER

Lisa is going on an exciting adventure in her time-travel submarine and she wants you to come along!

LOOK FOR LISA IN PREHISTORIC TIMES AND...

- ☐ Balloons (2)
- ☐ Bathtub
- ☐ Book
- ☐ Boot
- ☐ Bottle
- ☐ Broom
- ☐ Candle
- ☐ Clown
- ☐ Coffee pot
- ☐ Cup
- ☐ Egg
- ☐ Football
- ☐ Four-leaf clover
- ☐ Hammer
- ☐ Hockey stick
- ☐ Ice-cream cone
- ☐ Ladder
- ☐ Lamp
- ☐ Necktie
- ☐ Pizza
- ☐ Ring
- ☐ Scarecrow
- ☐ Sock
- ☐ Stars (2)
- ☐ String of pearls
- ☐ Sunglasses
- ☐ Tent
- ☐ Toothbrush
- ☐ Top hat
- ☐ Umbrella
- ☐ Used tire
- ☐ Wristwatch

What hasn't been invented yet?
What's in the cup?
Is there anything for rent?

Lisa has gone forward in time and she's landed in Count Dracula's home in Transylvania.

LOOK FOR LISA IN THIS CREEPY CASTLE AND...

- ☐ Axe
- ☐ Baseball
- ☐ Bones (6)
- ☐ Books (2)
- ☐ Boomerang
- ☐ Candles (6)
- ☐ Cracked mirror
- ☐ Dart
- ☐ Dustpan
- ☐ Envelope
- ☐ Fish
- ☐ Fish skeleton
- ☐ Heart
- ☐ Keys (3)
- ☐ Mallet
- ☐ Mice (4)
- ☐ Needle
- ☐ Number 13
- ☐ Pickles
- ☐ Rabbit
- ☐ Ring
- ☐ Roller skate
- ☐ Screwdriver
- ☐ Shovel
- ☐ Skateboard
- ☐ Skulls (5)
- ☐ Spoon
- ☐ Stake
- ☐ Steak
- ☐ Sword
- ☐ Tick-tack-toe
- ☐ Top hat
- ☐ Wind-up car
- ☐ Witch's hat
- ☐ Worms (2)
- ☐ Zipper

What is
   Uncle Nutzy?
What year is it?
Where is the garlic?

Next, Lisa travels to the year 1752. She's watching Benjamin Franklin as he proves that lightning is a form of electricity.

LOOK FOR LISA AT THIS HISTORIC HAPPENING AND...

- ☐ Arrow
- ☐ Basket
- ☐ Bell
- ☐ Bifocal eyeglasses
- ☐ Brushes (2)
- ☐ Bucket
- ☐ Cane
- ☐ Corn
- ☐ Deer
- ☐ Drums (2)
- ☐ Fish
- ☐ Flowerpot
- ☐ Frog
- ☐ Ghost
- ☐ Grapes
- ☐ Hair bows (5)
- ☐ Hammer
- ☐ Hearts (2)
- ☐ Hoop
- ☐ Keys (2)
- ☐ Kites (2)
- ☐ Ladder
- ☐ Mushroom
- ☐ Pumpkin
- ☐ Rabbit
- ☐ Ring
- ☐ Snail
- ☐ Snake
- ☐ Stamp
- ☐ Stars (3)
- ☐ Surfboard
- ☐ Tepee
- ☐ Turtle
- ☐ Umbrellas (3)
- ☐ Worm

What is Mrs. Franklin's first name?

What is the name of Franklin's almanac?

Wow! The time-travel sub has landed in the middle of the Ed Sullivan show where the Beatles are performing in America for the first time.

LOOK FOR LISA AS SHE ROCKS AND ROLLS AND...

- ☐ Balloons (2)
- ☐ Banjo
- ☐ Baton
- ☐ Bird
- ☐ Book
- ☐ Bow tie
- ☐ Bubblegum bubble
- ☐ Candle
- ☐ Chef
- ☐ Count Dracula
- ☐ Cymbals
- ☐ Dog
- ☐ Earmuffs
- ☐ Envelope
- ☐ Eyeglasses (3)
- ☐ Flower
- ☐ Football
- ☐ Ghost
- ☐ Giraffe
- ☐ Hearts (2)
- ☐ Kite
- ☐ Mouse
- ☐ Party hat
- ☐ Police officer
- ☐ Propeller
- ☐ Pumpkin
- ☐ Rabbit
- ☐ Skateboard
- ☐ Snowman
- ☐ Star
- ☐ Straw hat
- ☐ Tin man
- ☐ Wagon
- ☐ Witch
- ☐ Yo-yo

How many TV cameras are there? Where were the Beatles from?

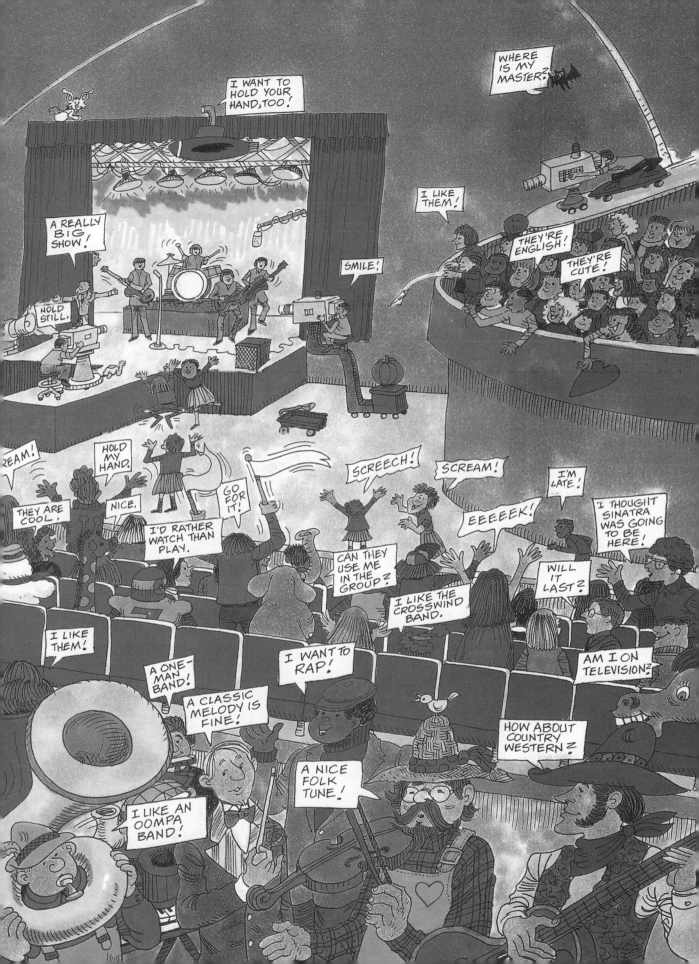

Lisa travels to Paris, France next, and arrives in the year 1902. She's in the laboratory of the first great female scientist, Madame Marie Curie.

LOOK FOR LISA AMONG THESE EXCITING EXPERIMENTS AND...

☐ Birds (2)
☐ Bone
☐ Book
☐ Broom
☐ Butterfly
☐ Cactus
☐ Candle
☐ Candy cane
☐ Carrot
☐ Clothespin
☐ Comb
☐ Compass
☐ Feather
☐ Ghost
☐ Hearts (2)
☐ Hot dog
☐ Ice-cream cone
☐ Igloo
☐ Keys (2)
☐ Mouse
☐ Nail
☐ Painted egg
☐ Pear
☐ Pencil
☐ Pie
☐ Rocket ship
☐ Roller skate
☐ Scissors
☐ Slice of pizza
☐ Straw
☐ Thermometer
☐ Toothbrush
☐ Tweezers

What is not dry yet?
What kind of pie is it?

Astronaut Neil Armstrong takes "a giant leap for mankind," as he thinks he's the first person to set foot on the moon. Little does he know, Lisa beat him to the moon walk!

LOOK FOR LISA IN THESE CAVERNOUS CRATERS AND...

- ☐ Airplane
- ☐ Apple
- ☐ Bat
- ☐ Book
- ☐ Bottle
- ☐ Camel
- ☐ Can
- ☐ Cat
- ☐ Chicken
- ☐ Cow
- ☐ Crown
- ☐ Dog
- ☐ Drum
- ☐ Flower
- ☐ Football
- ☐ Ghost
- ☐ Guitar
- ☐ Hammer
- ☐ Ice-cream cone
- ☐ Lips
- ☐ Mitten
- ☐ Owl
- ☐ Paintbrush
- ☐ Penguin
- ☐ Purse
- ☐ Rabbit
- ☐ Sailboat
- ☐ Seal
- ☐ Snake
- ☐ Stars (4)
- ☐ Tent
- ☐ Top hat
- ☐ Tree
- ☐ Umbrella
- ☐ Wreath

Can you find at least 12 more hidden things?

Lisa decides she wants her next trip to be a quiet sea voyage. But her time machine must have had something else in mind because Lisa has landed right in the middle of Captain Ahab's pursuit of Moby Dick!

LOOK FOR LISA IN THE OCEAN AND...

- ☐ Balloons (2)
- ☐ Beach ball
- ☐ Book
- ☐ Boomerang
- ☐ Bottle
- ☐ Candle
- ☐ Chef's hat
- ☐ Clown
- ☐ Drum
- ☐ Fire hydrant
- ☐ Fork
- ☐ Harp
- ☐ Harpoon
- ☐ Kerosene lamp
- ☐ Kite
- ☐ Lost sock
- ☐ Lunch box
- ☐ Mallet
- ☐ Mermaid
- ☐ Merman
- ☐ Oars (5)
- ☐ Pencil
- ☐ Picture frame
- ☐ Quarter moon
- ☐ Saw
- ☐ Shark fins (2)
- ☐ Spoon
- ☐ Stingray
- ☐ Stork
- ☐ Surfboard
- ☐ Telephone
- ☐ Tree
- ☐ Turtle
- ☐ Umbrella

What is the name of the whaling ship?

Lisa's time machine has traveled to a wedding party in the 1760s. Who's getting married? It's someone you may have heard of.

LOOK FOR LISA AT THIS SPECIAL CELEBRATION AND...

☐ Apple
☐ Arrow
☐ Banana
☐ Basket
☐ Boom box
☐ Broken wheel
☐ Broom
☐ Brush
☐ Elf
☐ Fiddle
☐ Fishing pole
☐ Flowerpot
☐ Fork
☐ Frog
☐ Gift
☐ Ice-cream cone
☐ Key
☐ Loaf of bread
☐ Mushroom
☐ Pear
☐ Pizza delivery
☐ Portable telephone
☐ Pumpkins (3)
☐ Rabbit
☐ Scarecrow
☐ Sherlock Holmes
☐ Skateboard
☐ Snake
☐ Soup
☐ Squirrel
☐ Top hat
☐ Wagons (2)
☐ Wedding cake
☐ Wooden spoon

What is Mrs. Boone's first name?
What's wrong with the table?

Lisa is now visiting the famous inventor, Thomas Edison, in his laboratory. Do you know some of the wonderful things he invented?

LOOK FOR LISA IN THE "WIZARD OF MENLO PARK'S" LAB AND…

- ☐ Ball
- ☐ Baseball cap
- ☐ Bird
- ☐ Bone
- ☐ Book
- ☐ Bucket
- ☐ Candle
- ☐ Doughnut
- ☐ Duck
- ☐ Feather
- ☐ Hard hat
- ☐ Hot dog
- ☐ Kerosene lamp
- ☐ Light bulb
- ☐ Milk container
- ☐ Mouse
- ☐ Pencils (2)
- ☐ Phonograph
- ☐ Picture frame
- ☐ Pillow
- ☐ Poodle
- ☐ Pumpkin
- ☐ Roller skates
- ☐ Safe
- ☐ Sailor's hat
- ☐ Screwdriver
- ☐ Ship
- ☐ Star
- ☐ Stool
- ☐ Sunglasses
- ☐ Typewriter
- ☐ Umbrella
- ☐ Wastepaper basket
- ☐ Wheel

What is the name of Edison's film?
Who can't read?

Lisa has pushed a few too many buttons and *zap-ping-kabaa* she's landed on a distant planet in the future!

LOOK FOR LISA AMONGST THESE FRIENDLY ALIENS AND...

- ☐ Apple
- ☐ Arrow
- ☐ Balloon
- ☐ Banana
- ☐ Bicycle horn
- ☐ Biplane
- ☐ Bone
- ☐ Bowling ball
- ☐ Bucket
- ☐ Captain Hook
- ☐ Clothespin
- ☐ Comb
- ☐ Cup
- ☐ Door
- ☐ Feather
- ☐ Fire hydrants (2)
- ☐ Flying saucer
- ☐ Football
- ☐ Guitar
- ☐ Heart
- ☐ Hot dog
- ☐ Ice skate
- ☐ Lock
- ☐ Nut
- ☐ Party hat
- ☐ Pie
- ☐ Sled
- ☐ Slice of pizza
- ☐ Slice of watermelon
- ☐ Space traffic cop
- ☐ Spoon
- ☐ Tepee
- ☐ Tire
- ☐ Watering can

What game is "it" late for?
What needs a target?

Lisa is trying to get back to our time zone. She's close…it's now 1925 and she's on stage at the Hippodrome Theater in New York City with the famous magician, Houdini.

LOOK FOR LISA BEFORE SHE DISAPPEARS AND…

- ☐ Balloon
- ☐ Baseball cap
- ☐ Bat
- ☐ Big apple
- ☐ Birds (2)
- ☐ Cane
- ☐ Carrot
- ☐ Chef
- ☐ Clown
- ☐ Count Dracula
- ☐ Crown
- ☐ Drum
- ☐ Duck
- ☐ Fish (2)
- ☐ Flowerpot
- ☐ Giraffe
- ☐ Graduate
- ☐ Helmet
- ☐ Jack-in-the-box
- ☐ Key
- ☐ Lion
- ☐ Mirror
- ☐ Palm tree
- ☐ Pig
- ☐ Ring
- ☐ Sailboat
- ☐ Sailor's hat
- ☐ Sled
- ☐ Snake
- ☐ Stars (5)
- ☐ Toothbrush
- ☐ Truck
- ☐ Whale

What did Houdini do in Australia? Where is the rabbit going?

Lisa has finally made it! She's back home with all of her "Where Are They?" friends.

LOOK FOR LISA AND...

- ☐ Bats (2)
- ☐ Bones (2)
- ☐ Clouds (3)
- ☐ Gift
- ☐ Hammers (2)
- ☐ Hearts (3)
- ☐ Hose
- ☐ Oar
- ☐ Octopus
- ☐ Question mark
- ☐ Stars (5)
- ☐ Sunglasses (3)
- ☐ Tulip
- ☐ Turtle
- ☐ Watering can

Who knew where Lisa was?

LOOK FOR LISA

Sylvester has run out of bamboo shoots to eat, but the mall should be the perfect place to buy some more.

SEARCH FOR SYLVESTER AT THIS MAD MALL AND...

- ☐ Banana peel
- ☐ Bird
- ☐ Birdhouse
- ☐ Bow and arrow
- ☐ Bowling ball
- ☐ Bride
- ☐ Cactus
- ☐ Convict
- ☐ Crown
- ☐ Dog
- ☐ Dracula
- ☐ Drum
- ☐ Feathers (2)
- ☐ Fish (2)
- ☐ Football
- ☐ Heart
- ☐ Ice-cream cone
- ☐ Jack-in-the-box
- ☐ Jack-o´-lantern
- ☐ Lion
- ☐ Moose
- ☐ Pig
- ☐ Rabbit
- ☐ Sailboat
- ☐ Santa Claus
- ☐ Star
- ☐ Surfboard
- ☐ Toy panda
- ☐ Trumpet
- ☐ Tuba
- ☐ Turtle
- ☐ Umbrella

Sylvester had no luck at the mall, so he figured he'd try the park next. Boy, was he getting hungry!

SEARCH FOR SYLVESTER IN THIS FUN-FILLED PLAYGROUND AND...

☐ Artist's model
☐ Balloons (3)
☐ Baseball cap
☐ Birds (4)
☐ Cactus
☐ Cat
☐ Chef's hat
☐ Clipboard
☐ Crown
☐ Drum
☐ Ducklings (4)
☐ Fish
☐ Fisherman
☐ Fork
☐ Genie
☐ Graduate
☐ Hammer
☐ Heart
☐ Mailbox
☐ Mouse
☐ Paintbrush
☐ Pencils (2)
☐ Postal carrier
☐ Rabbit
☐ Roller skates
☐ Saddle
☐ Sailboats (2)
☐ Saws (2)
☐ Scooter
☐ Squirrel
☐ Sunglasses
☐ Top hat
☐ Trash basket
☐ Umbrella

What's for rent?
What's the price of a
  pickle?

There were no bamboo shoots in the park, so Sylvester stopped off at a place where they serve almost anything!

SEARCH FOR SYLVESTER AT FAST FOOD HEAVEN AND...

- [ ] Arrows (2)
- [ ] Bone
- [ ] Cactus
- [ ] Cane
- [ ] Chef
- [ ] Crocodile
- [ ] Dogs (2)
- [ ] Drummer
- [ ] Earmuffs
- [ ] Elephants (2)
- [ ] Flying bat
- [ ] Flying carpet
- [ ] Flying saucer
- [ ] Fork
- [ ] Gas mask
- [ ] Ghosts (2)
- [ ] Green balloons (3)
- [ ] Igloo
- [ ] Kangaroo
- [ ] King
- [ ] Knight
- [ ] Lion
- [ ] Net
- [ ] Octopus
- [ ] Owl
- [ ] Pig
- [ ] Queen
- [ ] Santa Claus
- [ ] Skunk
- [ ] Squirrel
- [ ] Top hat
- [ ] Tuba
- [ ] Turtle
- [ ] Viking

Who hopes that the fish is fresh?

"The zoo should have bamboo shoots," thought Sylvester after he failed to find any at FAST FOOD HEAVEN. So off he went.

SEARCH FOR SYLVESTER AT THE ZANY ZOO AND…

☐ Artist
☐ Balloon
☐ Basket
☐ Bat and ball
☐ Bear
☐ Birds (2)
☐ Brooms (2)
☐ Buzzard
☐ Candy cane
☐ Cook
☐ Crown
☐ Dracula
☐ Duck
☐ Flamingo
☐ Graduate
☐ Ice-cream cones (2)
☐ Key
☐ Monkey
☐ Mouse
☐ Painted egg
☐ Pencils (2)
☐ Penguin
☐ "Polly"
☐ Rabbit
☐ Rooster
☐ Sailboat
☐ Seahorse
☐ Spoon
☐ Toucan
☐ Toy ship

Who doesn't know?
Who is going back to Transylvania?

Sylvester had no luck finding bamboo shoots at the zoo, but his next stop is the ABCD school lunchroom. He's sure to find bamboo shoots there.

SEARCH FOR
SYLVESTER
IN THIS
ALPHABETICAL
SCHOOL AND…

- [ ] A
- [ ] B
- [ ] C
- [ ] D
- [ ] E
- [ ] F
- [ ] G
- [ ] H
- [ ] I
- [ ] J
- [ ] K
- [ ] L
- [ ] M
- [ ] N
- [ ] O
- [ ] P
- [ ] Q
- [ ] R
- [ ] S
- [ ] T
- [ ] U
- [ ] V
- [ ] W
- [ ] X
- [ ] Y
- [ ] Z
- [ ] Baseball cap
- [ ] Eyeglasses
- [ ] Spoon

What kind of prehistoric animal is it?

They were not serving bamboo shoots for lunch, but as Sylvester was leaving he heard cheering coming from the gym. "Maybe, they're selling bamboo shoots in there," he thought.

SEARCH FOR SYLVESTER AT THE BASKETBALL GAME AND...

- ☐ Baskets (2)
- ☐ Bird
- ☐ Bone
- ☐ Book
- ☐ Bunny
- ☐ Cleats
- ☐ Clown
- ☐ Dogs (2)
- ☐ Doughnut
- ☐ Elephant
- ☐ Envelopes (2)
- ☐ Fish
- ☐ Flower
- ☐ Football
- ☐ Frog
- ☐ Glove
- ☐ Horn
- ☐ Ice skate
- ☐ Ice-cream cone
- ☐ Juggler
- ☐ Mouse
- ☐ Necktie
- ☐ Popcorn
- ☐ Roller skates
- ☐ Sailor's cap
- ☐ Saw
- ☐ Slice of pizza
- ☐ Snake
- ☐ Stars (3)
- ☐ Toy arrow
- ☐ Whistle

Who wants to play, too?
Who is winning?

Not a single bamboo shoot was sold at the game. Sylvester was starving. He passed an old haunted house where someone was cooking. Could they be making bamboo shoots?

SEARCH FOR SYLVESTER AT THIS SPOOKY MANSION AND…

☐ Apple
☐ Arrows (2)
☐ Banana
☐ Bone
☐ Button
☐ Can
☐ Cook
☐ Cup
☐ Cupcake
☐ Fire hydrant
☐ Flashlight
☐ Flowerpot
☐ Heart
☐ Ice-cream soda
☐ Jack-o´-lantern
☐ Keyboard
☐ Kite
☐ Mask
☐ Medal
☐ Old shoe
☐ Pencil
☐ Pie
☐ Pot
☐ Rat
☐ Ring
☐ Skateboard
☐ Skulls (2)
☐ Sled
☐ Street light
☐ Sword
☐ Swordfish
☐ Trash can
☐ Turtle
☐ Umbrella

Sylvester didn't enter the haunted house, and now he was really, really hungry. "Maybe Detective Donald can help me detect bamboo shoots," thought Sylvester.

SEARCH FOR SYLVESTER AT DETECTIVE DONALD'S DIGS AND...

- ☐ Apple core
- ☐ Beard and glasses disguise
- ☐ Blackboard
- ☐ Bomb
- ☐ Boot
- ☐ Broken legs (2)
- ☐ Broken pencils (3)
- ☐ Buckets (2)
- ☐ Candles (3)
- ☐ Cupcake
- ☐ Dart
- ☐ Deflated balloon
- ☐ Dumbbell
- ☐ Eraser
- ☐ Feather
- ☐ Fish
- ☐ Fly swatter
- ☐ Footprints
- ☐ Graduation cap
- ☐ Hamburger
- ☐ Hockey stick
- ☐ Hole in a shoe
- ☐ Hooks (3)
- ☐ Hourglass
- ☐ Ink bottle
- ☐ Mirror
- ☐ Mouse
- ☐ Owl
- ☐ Paintbrush
- ☐ Record
- ☐ Ring
- ☐ Roller skate
- ☐ Slice of pizza
- ☐ Stars (3)

Detective Donald advised Sylvester to look under the big top for bamboo shoots.

SEARCH FOR SYLVESTER AT THIS SILLY CIRCUS AND...

- ☐ Baker
- ☐ Banana
- ☐ Bat
- ☐ Bearded man
- ☐ Binoculars
- ☐ Candy cane
- ☐ Carrot
- ☐ Clothespins (3)
- ☐ Cup
- ☐ Dog
- ☐ Elephants (2)
- ☐ Feather
- ☐ Fire hydrant
- ☐ Giraffe
- ☐ Hot dog
- ☐ Humpty Dumpty
- ☐ Ice skates
- ☐ Ice-cream cone
- ☐ Kangaroo
- ☐ Lamp
- ☐ Mice (2)
- ☐ Mother Goose
- ☐ Paint bucket
- ☐ Paper bag
- ☐ Periscope
- ☐ Pig
- ☐ Pillow
- ☐ Rabbit
- ☐ Seals (2)
- ☐ Skunk
- ☐ Slice of watermelon
- ☐ Stars (5)
- ☐ Top hat
- ☐ Turtle
- ☐ Umbrella
- ☐ Unicorn
- ☐ Watering can
- ☐ Wizard

Who lost his costume?

Sylvester had no luck at the circus, but on his way home he spotted a hot air balloon about to take off. "From up there I'll be able to find bamboo shoots," thought Sylvester.

SEARCH FOR SYLVESTER AS HE SOARS THROUGH THE SKY AND...

- ☐ Alien spaceship
- ☐ Ape
- ☐ Apple
- ☐ Arrows (2)
- ☐ Books (2)
- ☐ Bowling balls (2)
- ☐ Broom
- ☐ Candy canes (2)
- ☐ Chef
- ☐ Clowns (2)
- ☐ Coffeepot
- ☐ Cup
- ☐ Ducks (2)
- ☐ Firecracker
- ☐ Fish (2)
- ☐ Fishing pole
- ☐ Flowerpot
- ☐ Footballs (2)
- ☐ Hearts (2)
- ☐ Horns (2)
- ☐ Hose
- ☐ Hot dog
- ☐ Light bulb
- ☐ Lips
- ☐ Magnifying glasses (2)
- ☐ Painted eggs (2)
- ☐ Pencil
- ☐ Pillow
- ☐ Slices of watermelon (2)
- ☐ Telescopes (2)
- ☐ Tires (2)
- ☐ Turtles (2)

Who is the witch talking to?

From way up above Sylvester saw his old neighborhood. "That's it!" thought Sylvester. "I should have known to go back home to mom."

SEARCH FOR SYLVESTER IN BAMBOO TOWN AND...

☐ Apple
☐ Artist
☐ Backpack
☐ Birds (3)
☐ Bone
☐ Bucket
☐ Cactus
☐ Cash register
☐ Cat
☐ Crowns (2)
☐ Dogs (2)
☐ Elephant
☐ Feather
☐ Fish (3)
☐ Hammer
☐ Hoe
☐ Key
☐ Kiddie pool
☐ Mailbox
☐ Mushroom
☐ Photographer
☐ Pie
☐ Pitcher
☐ Pitchfork
☐ Pumpkin
☐ Scarecrow
☐ Scissors
☐ Scooter
☐ Screwdriver
☐ Sword
☐ Tricycle
☐ Turtles (2)
☐ Umbrella

What is the name of the street?
Who is "Captain Bamboo"?

Sylvester ate all the bamboo shoots he wanted yesterday, but today he woke up hungry again!

SEARCH FOR SYLVESTER AND...

☐ Candy cane
☐ Envelope
☐ Flamingo
☐ Flying bat
☐ Hearts (2)
☐ Horseshoe
☐ Light bulb
☐ Mushroom
☐ Musical notes (2)
☐ Painted eggs (2)
☐ Picture
☐ Pitcher
☐ Raccoon
☐ Stars (2)

SEARCH FOR SYLVESTER

Wendy is a typical teenager — with one small difference — she's a witch. Like other kids her age, she attends school. *Un*like other kids her age, she attends a very special school — a school for witches!

FIND WENDY AT WITCHVILLE HIGH SCHOOL AND...

- ☐ Arrow
- ☐ Balloon
- ☐ Bear
- ☐ Blue-eyed monster
- ☐ Bones (3)
- ☐ Book
- ☐ Broken window
- ☐ Brooms (6)
- ☐ Candle
- ☐ Candy cane
- ☐ Costume
- ☐ Elephant
- ☐ Fish (3)
- ☐ Fishbowl
- ☐ Green-eyed monster
- ☐ Horseshoe
- ☐ Kettles (2)
- ☐ Key
- ☐ Kites (2)
- ☐ Lost shoe
- ☐ Mummy
- ☐ Mushrooms (3)
- ☐ Owl
- ☐ Pig
- ☐ Principal
- ☐ Pumpkin
- ☐ Question-mark hat
- ☐ Rabbit
- ☐ Schoolbag
- ☐ Skulls (3)
- ☐ Snake
- ☐ Star
- ☐ "Thirteen" (3)

What is the cobweb collection for?
What time do classes start?

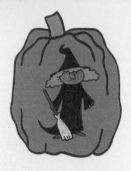

It's another typical day at Witchville High. In this class the young witches are learning their witchcraft. However, Wendy doesn't seem too interested in learning how to be a witch.

LOOK FOR WENDY IN THE CLASSROOM AND...

- ☐ Apples (2)
- ☐ Axe
- ☐ Banana peel
- ☐ Baseball
- ☐ Bow
- ☐ Broken mirror
- ☐ Brooms (3)
- ☐ Bugs (2)
- ☐ Candles (3)
- ☐ Cupcake
- ☐ Dead flowers
- ☐ Fish
- ☐ Flower
- ☐ Flying bats (2)
- ☐ Ghost
- ☐ Hamburger
- ☐ Hammer
- ☐ Heart
- ☐ Hourglass
- ☐ Ice skates
- ☐ Marshmallow
- ☐ Mouse
- ☐ Octopus
- ☐ Paper airplane
- ☐ Roller skates
- ☐ Scissors
- ☐ Screwdriver
- ☐ Ski
- ☐ Skulls (3)
- ☐ Skunk
- ☐ Snake
- ☐ Spool of thread
- ☐ Turtle
- ☐ Worm

What time is it?
Which witch drew the picture?

Hooray!! It's class trip day! Where are Wendy and her witchy friends going? To a haunted house, of course!

SEARCH FOR WENDY ON THE WITCHES' CLASS TRIP AND...

- ☐ Apple
- ☐ Basket
- ☐ Basketball
- ☐ Bird
- ☐ Bones (2)
- ☐ Cactus
- ☐ Candle
- ☐ Chair
- ☐ Chicken
- ☐ Crayon
- ☐ Crocodile
- ☐ Dogs (2)
- ☐ Faucet
- ☐ Flowers (2)
- ☐ Flying bat
- ☐ Football
- ☐ Ghost
- ☐ Hearts (2)
- ☐ Hockey stick
- ☐ Hot dogs (2)
- ☐ Ice-cream cone
- ☐ Ice skate
- ☐ Mitten
- ☐ Mouse
- ☐ Paintbrush
- ☐ Paint bucket
- ☐ Painted egg
- ☐ Periscope
- ☐ Pizza slice
- ☐ Sailor cap
- ☐ Saw
- ☐ Skulls (2)
- ☐ Squirrel
- ☐ Sunglasses (2)
- ☐ Tombstone
- ☐ Top hat
- ☐ Turtles (3)
- ☐ Watermelon slice

Which witch had her hair done?

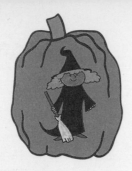

Wendy's favorite time of day is lunch time. The food at Witchville High is not too different from the food at most schools.

FIND WENDY IN THE LUNCHROOM AND...

- ☐ Banana peel
- ☐ Bat
- ☐ Black cat
- ☐ Bone
- ☐ Books (2)
- ☐ Bowling ball
- ☐ Brooms (2)
- ☐ Chef's hat
- ☐ Clothespin
- ☐ Crown
- ☐ Crystal ball
- ☐ Empty bowl
- ☐ Eyeglasses
- ☐ Feather
- ☐ Fish (2)
- ☐ Fork
- ☐ Frog
- ☐ Ghost
- ☐ Graduate
- ☐ Hatched egg
- ☐ Ice skate
- ☐ Mouse
- ☐ Musicians (4)
- ☐ Necktie
- ☐ Pig
- ☐ Rabbits (2)
- ☐ Radio
- ☐ Sailor cap
- ☐ Snakes (2)
- ☐ Sock
- ☐ "Spot"
- ☐ Straw hat
- ☐ Sunglasses
- ☐ Tea kettle
- ☐ Trash can
- ☐ Waiter

Which witch has a bandage?
Which witch has a bow?

Final exams are lots of fun with this bunch of wacky witches! Wendy is happy just watching her classmates displaying their witchy ways.

LOOK FOR WENDY DURING FINAL EXAMS AND...

- ☐ Apples (5)
- ☐ Baseball bat
- ☐ Bell
- ☐ Bird
- ☐ Birdcage
- ☐ Bones (5)
- ☐ Book
- ☐ Candles (2)
- ☐ Cat
- ☐ Clipboards (4)
- ☐ Fish (2)
- ☐ Flower
- ☐ Hose
- ☐ Ice-cream cone
- ☐ Kite
- ☐ Lock
- ☐ Mitten
- ☐ Necklace
- ☐ Owl
- ☐ Painted egg
- ☐ Pear
- ☐ Periscope
- ☐ Pillow
- ☐ Pogo stick
- ☐ Purse
- ☐ Roller skates
- ☐ Sailboat
- ☐ Skis
- ☐ Skulls (2)
- ☐ Snake
- ☐ Soccer ball
- ☐ Telephone
- ☐ Umbrella
- ☐ Watering can
- ☐ Witch doctor

Which witch can make her hair stand up?
Which witch has an apple?

Graduation day has finally arrived. Now all these fine young witches will start looking for witches' work. Wendy wonders what her first job will be.

HUNT FOR WENDY AT GRADUATION AND...

☐ Arrow
☐ Balloons (4)
☐ Banana peel
☐ Bomb
☐ Cane
☐ Eyeglasses
☐ Firecrackers (2)
☐ Fish
☐ Flying bats (2)
☐ Hearts (3)
☐ Hot dog
☐ Humpty Dumpty
☐ Ice-cream pop
☐ Ice skates
☐ Igloo
☐ Leaping lizard
☐ Mailbox
☐ Manhole cover
☐ Mary Poppins
☐ Misplaced flowerpot
☐ Mouse
☐ Paint bucket
☐ Panda
☐ Periscope
☐ Pie
☐ Pillow
☐ Pizza
☐ Pumpkins (2)
☐ Record
☐ Robot
☐ Sleeping witches (2)
☐ Stocking cap
☐ Tepee
☐ Turtle
☐ Vulture
☐ Worm

Who is the school dropout?
Who wasn't invited?

Wendy gets a job at the Count's castle. What is she doing?!? Instead of witching around, she's cleaning! The Count and his creepy friends are not happy. Better look for work someplace else, Wendy.

FIND WENDY IN COUNT DRACULA'S LIVING ROOM AND...

- ☐ Apple
- ☐ Bones (2)
- ☐ Brooms (3)
- ☐ Candles (2)
- ☐ Candy cane
- ☐ Dog
- ☐ Fish
- ☐ Flying bats (5)
- ☐ Football
- ☐ Ghosts (2)
- ☐ Globe
- ☐ Hearts (3)
- ☐ Hot dog
- ☐ Ice skate
- ☐ One-eyed monster
- ☐ Painted egg
- ☐ Palm tree
- ☐ Piano keys
- ☐ Pick
- ☐ Quarter moons (2)
- ☐ Skull
- ☐ Snail
- ☐ Star
- ☐ Straw
- ☐ Tombstones (2)
- ☐ Tulip
- ☐ Umbrellas (3)
- ☐ Wreath
- ☐ Yo-Yo

What is Dracula's favorite fruit?
Where did the flowers come from?
Who is moving to the Vampire State Building?

Wendy's next job is assisting Dr. Frankenstein. She's cleaned and organized his laboratory, and spruced up Frankenstein's monster! She probably won't last too long here, either.

SEARCH FOR WENDY IN DR. FRANKENSTEIN'S LABORATORY AND...

☐ Apple
☐ Baseball
☐ Bell
☐ Bone
☐ Book
☐ Cactus
☐ Candy cane
☐ Dancer
☐ Fish
☐ Flowers (2)
☐ Flying bat
☐ Ghost
☐ Hat
☐ Mice (4)
☐ Music notes (4)
☐ Oil can
☐ Pear
☐ Pencil
☐ Pillow
☐ Roller skates
☐ Screwdriver
☐ Skulls (2)
☐ Snake
☐ Socks (3)
☐ Speakers (2)
☐ Straw
☐ Suspenders (2 pairs)
☐ Tick-tack-toe
☐ Toast
☐ Vulture
☐ Welcome mat

How high can the monster jump?
What did Fritz drop?

Wendy finds another job —in a mummy's tomb! She decides to redecorate the tomb with plants and flowers. However, the mummy is not amused. In fact, he's very upset! Wendy has done it again. She just can't behave in a witchlike way.

HUNT FOR WENDY IN THE MUMMY'S TOMB AND...

- ☐ Airplane
- ☐ Award
- ☐ Bell
- ☐ Bird
- ☐ Butterfly
- ☐ Clown
- ☐ Duck
- ☐ Elephant
- ☐ Fish
- ☐ Hammer
- ☐ Heart
- ☐ Hose
- ☐ Ice-cream cone
- ☐ Ice skate
- ☐ Key
- ☐ Kite
- ☐ Lion
- ☐ Lobster
- ☐ Mushroom
- ☐ Necktie
- ☐ Painted egg
- ☐ Quarter moon
- ☐ Rabbit
- ☐ Ring
- ☐ Rooster
- ☐ Sailboat
- ☐ Sea horse
- ☐ Seal
- ☐ Snowman
- ☐ Sock
- ☐ Starfish
- ☐ Tepee
- ☐ Tiger
- ☐ Umbrella
- ☐ Worm

Who wants a peanut?

All of Wendy's "Where Are They?" friends have come to visit her jack-o'-lantern farm.

LOOK FOR:

- ☐ Bone
- ☐ Boot
- ☐ Brooms (3)
- ☐ Canes (2)
- ☐ Chicken
- ☐ Crayon
- ☐ Flowers (2)
- ☐ Heart
- ☐ Mouse
- ☐ Mushroom
- ☐ Nail
- ☐ Smallest jack-o'-lantern

WHERE'S WENDY?